Fantastic Worlds

By Stan Cullimore

Contents

Section 1
The Moon Mouse   2

Section 2
The Land of Custard   12

Section 3
Little Bee   22

Longman

The Moon Mouse

One day Abbie went into the kitchen.
"Mum, can I have a pet?"

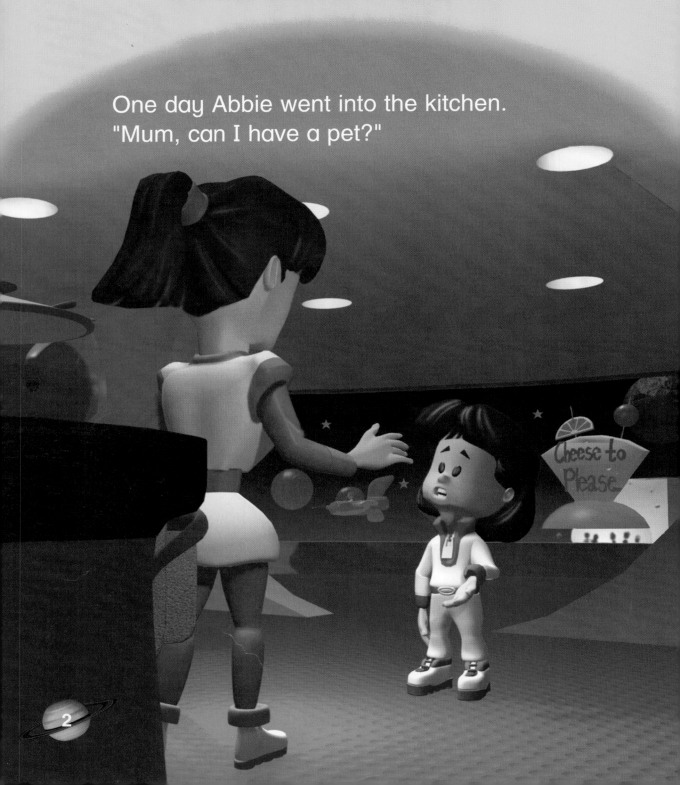

"No, you can't," said Mum.
"I hate living on the moon," said Abbie.

"Why?" asked Mum.
"Because I can't have a pet," said Abbie.

"What do you want to eat?" asked Mum.
"Not cheese! I am sick of cheese!" Abbie said.

"Cheese is good for you," said Mum.
"No, cheese is good for mice," Abbie smiled.

Mum opened the cupboard. She shook her head.
"That's funny," she said.
"What is?" asked Abbie.

"The cheese has gone," said Mum. "Someone has eaten it all."
Mum went to the sink.

Abbie looked at the cupboard. She smiled.
She ran over to the cupboard and picked
something up.

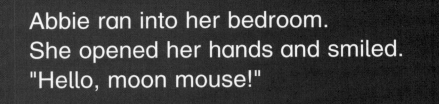

Abbie ran into her bedroom.
She opened her hands and smiled.
"Hello, moon mouse!"

"You can be my pet!" Abbie said. "I'll get you lots more cheese!"
The moon mouse squeaked. He liked cheese!

The Land of Custard

Ian walked over the wobbly yellow grass.
There was a boy playing on the swings.
"Hello, I'm Jack," said the boy.

"Do you want to play on the swings?" asked Jack.
"Yes, please." Ian sat down on the swing.
He began to swing backwards and forwards.

Ian looked around. "That's funny."
"What is?" asked Jack.
"The swing is all wobbly," said Ian.

Jack jumped off the swing. "Let's go and play on the climbing frame instead."
The two boys ran over to the climbing frame.

They started to climb. Ian got to the top and rubbed his tummy.
"I'm hungry," he said.
"So am I," said Jack.

"What can we eat?" asked Ian.
"How about the climbing frame?" said Jack.
"What?"

Jack smiled. "This is the land of custard. You
can eat anything you want."
He opened his mouth and he took a big bite.
Then he took another and another.

Ian opened his mouth. He took a big bite, too.
"It's made of custard!"
Jack nodded.

Ian took another bite. Then another.

Then … he woke up. He was at home in his own jelly bed and he was eating his own jelly pillow!

Little Bee

Little Bee flew over to her mum.
"Mum," she said. "I don't want to be a busy bee."
Mum smiled. "Well you can be a worker bee
like me."

Big Sister looked up from her paper.
"Don't be silly, Little Bee. You don't want to be
a worker bee. They stay at home and look after
the hive. You want to be a busy bee, like me."

"What do busy bees do?" asked Little Bee.
"I'll show you," replied Big Sister.
She took down a book of photos.

"This is a photo of me flying into a flower."
"Why are you doing that?" asked Little Bee.
"I'll show you," replied Big Sister. She turned
the page.

"This is a photo of me taking nectar from the flower," said Big Sister.
"Why do you want the nectar?" asked Little Bee.
"I'll show you," replied Big Sister. She turned the page.

"This is a photo of me taking the nectar into the hive," said Big Sister.
"What happens to the nectar?" asked Little Bee.
"I'll tell you," said Mum.

"The worker bees turn the nectar into honey,"
she said.
Little Bee licked her lips. "That sounds like fun.
I love honey. I want to be a worker bee."

"Don't be silly. You have to be a busy bee like me," said Big Sister. "You can come to work with me tomorrow."
Little Bee went to bed feeling sad.

The next day Little Bee went to work with
Big Sister.
"Let's go into that flower," said Big Sister.
As soon as they got inside the flower Little Bee
began to sneeze.
She sneezed again and again and again.

"Oh dear, Little Bee. You can't be a busy bee like me if the flowers make you sneeze all the time," said Big Sister.
Little Bee smiled. "Good. Now I'll have to be a worker bee and make honey all day!"

Little Bee flew back to the hive to tell Mum her good news.

"Mum!" she shouted, "I've got hay fever. I can be a worker bee after all!"